THE  IF... FILES

BOING

THE IF... FILES

Steve Bell

Methuen

For Heather, William, Joey, Paddy, Kitkat and Percy.

Published by Methuen 1997

Cartoons first published in the *Guardian* in 1995, 1996 and 1997

This collection first published in the United Kingdom in 1997 by Methuen, Random House 20 Vauxhall Bridge Road, London SW1V 2SA

Random House Australia (Pty) Limited 20 Alfred Street, Milsons Point, Sydney New South Wales 2061, Australia

Random House New Zealand Limited 18 Poland Road, Glenfield Auckland 10, New Zealand

Random House South Africa (Pty) Limited Endulini, 5A Jubilee Road, Parktown 2193, South Africa

Random House UK Limited Reg. No. 954009

Design by Brian Homer
Production by Trevor Carter
Edited by Steve Bell and Brian Homer

A CIP catalogue for this book is available from the British Library

ISBN 0 413 72230 9

Printed and bound in Great Britain by Scotprint Ltd, Musselburgh, Scotland

IF... Contents

Big Ones:

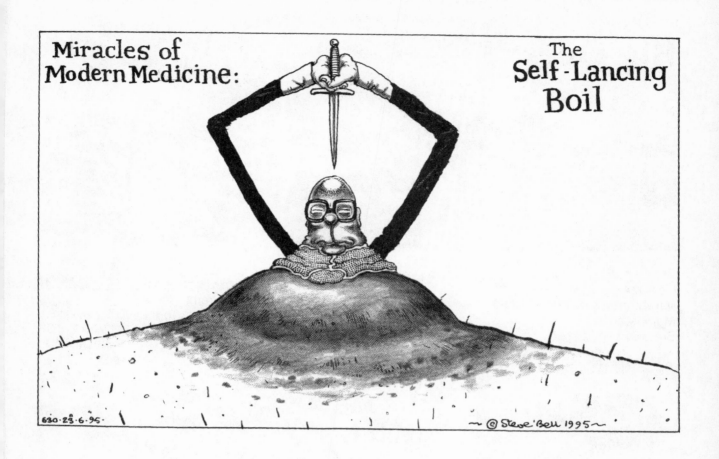

8

10

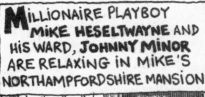

13

14

AUTHENTIC RECENT PICTURE OF **BORIS YELTSIN** AND **DENG XIAO PING** CYCLING IN CENTRAL ASIA

THE **QUEEN MOTHER**, **BORIS YELTSIN**, **DENG XIAO PING** AND THE **BRITISH ECONOMY** PAUSING FOR BREATH DURING A RECENT **STEP-AEROBICS** WORK OUT. © **AUTHENTIPIX UK** plc.

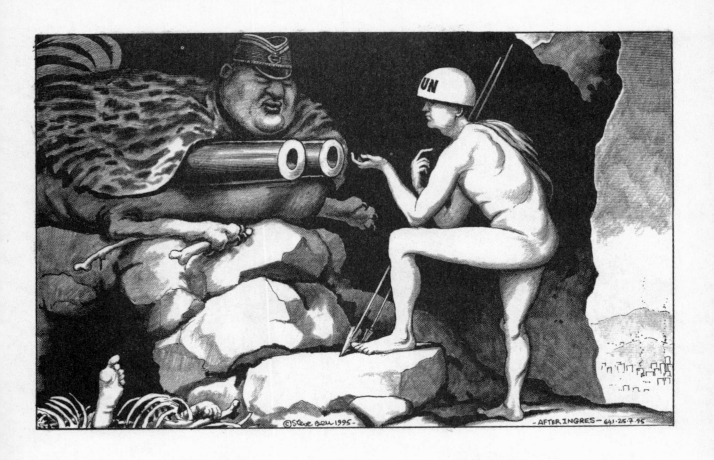

— AFTER INGRES — 641·25·7·95

ETHNIC CLEANSING

ETHNIC DRY·CLEANING

653·15·9·95 —

18

19

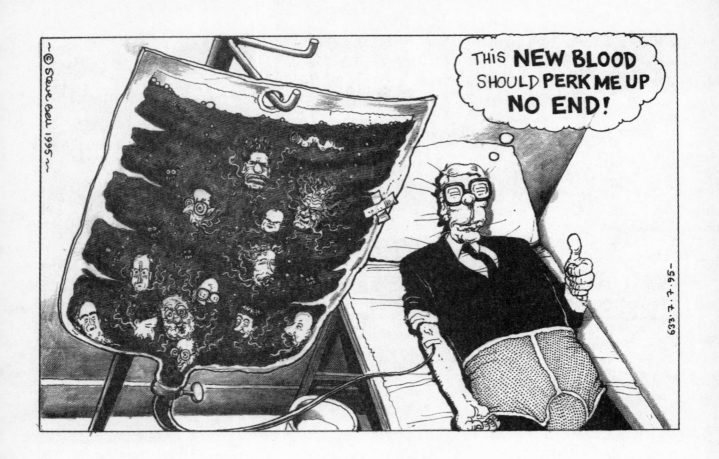

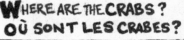

WHERE ARE THE CRABS? OÙ SONT LES CRABES?

BLASTED BY THE UNIMAGINABLE FORCE OF THE WHALEFART...

THRUST INTO THE STRATOSPHERE ....

CARRIED ROUND THE WORLD ON THE JETSTREAM

...DEPOSITED OVER WESTERN EUROPE

— © Steve Bell 1995 —

MORE SHARM- -PIE-NYAH, CHERIE?

AïEEE! AïEEE! CRABES!! CRABES!!

SKRAKS

NON! NO CRABES, CHERIE! I 'AVE A BIDET AND A SCRURBING BRURSH!!

AïEEEE!! ERRRGUE!

© Steve Bell 1995

AHHHH...

THE INVIGORATINGUE SMELL OF NUCLEAIRE WHALEFART®™

I MURST RING MY BEST FRIEND 'ELMUT!

'ELMUT! MON AMI! WOULD YOU LIKE TO USE SOME OF MY WHALEFART ™®?

'ELMUT - FOR YEARS WE FRENCH 'AVE TRAINED URP AN ELITE FORCE OF RARE NUCLEAIRE-FED FARTINGUE WHALES...

...AND NOW I WANT MY EURO-PALS TO ENJOY THE BENEFITS!

ONE FRAPPE OF WHALEFART®™ IN THE RAGHT PLACE AND ALL YOUR ENNEMIS WILL RURN AWAY!!

ALONG WITH A FEW FAIR-WEATHAIRE FRIENDS ....

PONK

© Steve Bell 95

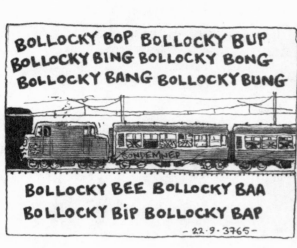

BOLLOCKY BOP BOLLOCKY BUP
BOLLOCKY BING BOLLOCKY BONG
BOLLOCKY BANG BOLLOCKY BUNG

CONDEMNED

BOLLOCKY BEE BOLLOCKY BAA
BOLLOCKY BIP BOLLOCKY BAP

– 22·9·3765 –

BOLLOCKY BOO
BOLLOCKY BOOO

NO LIGHTS, NO WINDOWS, NO SCENERY, NO DUTY FREE

BOLLOCKY BOO
BOLLOCKY BOOOO

BOLLOCKY BOOOO
THIS IS THE LAST TIME I TAKE THE 'BOLLOCKS UNLIMITED' ™ TO MONTE CARLO!!

BOLLOCKY BOOO
BOLLOCKY BOOOO

© Steve Bell 95

WOW! WE'RE IN FRANCE!

BOGGLER BOGGLER

NO, WE'RE IN FOLKESTONE. SIT ON THIS SIDING AND DON'T MOVE!

...I'M GOING TO BLAG OUR WAY THROUGH THE BIG HOLE....

© Steve Bell 95

25·9·3766 –

MERDE! 'OW CAN I GET THIS BIG BOX OF DRURGS THROUGH TO LA FRANCE?

HMMM...THAT STUPIDE LOOKING TRAIN GIVES ME UN IDÉE!

'EY, TRAIN – I AM A CUSTOMS INSPECTEUR AND I WANT TO INSPECT YOUR TONSILLES... SAY AAAAAAHHH!

AAAAAAGLLLP....

TOSS

© Steve Bell '95 –

26·9·3767 –

THROB

IT'S OK – I EXPLAINED THAT WE'RE A COMMERCIALLY SENSITIVE PART OF THE ANGLO-FRENCH NUCLEAR MUTANT ENGINE EXCHANGE PROGRAMME!

SNOOT

...WE JUST HAVE TO WAIT FOR AN ELECTRIC ENGINE.... BARRY? ARE YOU FEELING OK??

BOGGLER THROB BOGGLER THROB BOGGLER BOGGLER THROB THROB

BARRY! WAIT! WE'RE NOT READY TO.... STOP! STOP!!

GRROWWL

WAAAAAA AAAAA AAAAA

27·9·3768 –

© Steve Bell '95 –

25

26

CHRIST!!
WHERE'S
HIS PANTS??

Today you can't see my pants....

...but I can see you!!!

"I WAS THERE!" by Humphrey the Cat

©Steve Bell 1995

I knew it! he's just forgotten to tuck his jacket in!

17-10-3682 ©Steve Bell 1995

Thank God some of us have still got standards!

My Arse!!

©The Bellworks 1995

Our Nation's Future
Conservative
The Pant is falling

18-10-3683 ©The Bellworks 1995

©Steve Bell 1995

Good morning ladies and gentlemen. I am a John Major replicant.......

"If you keep pointing that thing at me, I'm going to have to tell Norma....."

...and you may ask me any question you wish about the Prime Minister's speech....

"...and then I'll scream and scream!! Now, off you jolly well fuck!!!"

...so long as your questions are neither interesting nor rude nor awkward nor challenging......

"Scusi pliz, we are registered aliens and we would like very much copy of Jona Maiora spitch now pliz...?"

"Yes, will the Prime Minister be able to go a whole hour without having to go to the toilet?"

"Oh Glory!!! This is the moment I've spun for all year! Johnny be good now now ,wo wo!!!"

19-10-3684

"Excuse me, but this is a top-secret Written-Press-only briefing. Put that camera away now please!"

©Steve Bell/The Bellworks 1995

"HEY, PEOPLE! HAVE I EVER LET YOU DOWN YET????"

"It's no use John — everybody still thinks you're sad and useless!"

"Well, ladies and gentlemen, it looks like I've got me bang to rights!"

20-10-3685

In the words of the small town solicitor: **Stitcham, Hangham & Bangham!!**

Any further questions?

Sir, could you tell us how much your wife's handcuffs cost?

I know where you live.

©Steve Bell/The Bellworks 1995~

HUMPHREY! SO GLAD YOU COULD MAKE IT... SOCKS!

IT'S AN HONOUR TO MEET THE MOST POWER-FUL CAT ON EARTH! PROOT

LIKEWISE IT'S AN HONOUR FOR ME TO MEET THE MOST INTELLIGENT CREATURE ON DOWNING ST! FROONT!

LET'S SEE IF TOGETHER WE CAN'T SORT OUT THIS NORTHERN IRELAND CRAP!!

— 23·10·3686 —

— © Steve Bell 1995 —

WHO'S THE GOON IN THE BOWLER HAT WHO FOLLOWED YOU IN?? 24·10·3687-

THAT'S TRIMBLE. WE'RE KEEPING AN EYE ON EACH OTHER.... ..WATCH THIS!...

SOCKS—THERE ARE OTHER THINGS IN ULSTER THAN FISH, WOULDN'T YOU AGREE? I'M NOT SURE

STOP THAT TALKING IN CODE, YOU FENIAN FELINE FIEND!! SNUK

©Steve Bell'95

25·10·3688— ©Steve Bell 1995—

CHRIST! THEY'RE ALL HERE THIS WEEK: YELTSIN, TRIMBLE...

EY! I YELOFF YORR POOSSY!

HEH HEH!! KOM OOP YEND SEE ME SOM TIME

GOOD GOD! THAT FOREIGNER TWEAKED MY REAR!

...BRING YORR PETSK! YOHOHOHO!! BUMP

...AND NOW HE'S TALKING IN CODE!

34

THIS FAMILY'S A **DISGRACE!!** THERE ARE **SKIDMARKS** ON THE **TABLECLOTH!** MY FEET ARE **STICKING** TO THE **FLOOR!**....

MY **WIFE'S** NOT EVEN **MARRIED** TO ME!.... MY **DAUGHTER'S SHACKED** UP WITH A **RAT!!**

HEY!

**** OFF!

MY **SON** SPENDS HIS LIFE TRAWLING THE INTERNET FOR **PORN** AND MY **COUSIN'S** A **RAGING POOFTER!**

**** RIGHT OFF, DAD!

STUFF YOU, MAN!!

THERE'S ONLY **ONE WAY OUT!** – I'M GONNA SEND MY **GRANDSON** TO A **RELIGIOUS SCHOOL!**

1·11·3693 – ©Steve Bell 1995 –

BARKING MONKS ACADEMY

STRICTLY NON-SELECTIVE

OVER-ACHIEVING NOB-CHILDREN ONLY

HERE WE ARE!

I WANT YOU TO **LEARN** MY BOY SOME **MORALS**, GOT THAT?

QUITE, QUITE, I JUST HAVE **TWO** QUESTIONS:

ARE YOUR PARENTS **MOVERS AND SHAKERS**, AND HOW MUCH DO THEY **EARN??**

I THINK THEY'RE **SCREAMERS**, SIR

©Steve Bell 1995 –

YIP YIP!

OWOOOO!

PSSST! – D'YOU NEED ANYTHING TO KILL THE PAIN OF **EXTRA HOMEWORK?**

BARKING MONKS ACADEMY

..UPPERS, DOWNERS, HAIL MARYS.... ..**OH NO!!** IT'S THE **VATICAN HIT SQUAD!**

EVERYBODY UP AGAINST **DA WALL! DA HOLY FUDDER'S** BEEN LOOKIN' AT DA FIGURES ON DIS PLACE.....

YOUR **SPIRITUAL ATTAIN-MENT TEST** RESULTS ARE **CRAP!** FROM NOW ON DA UNIFORM IS **HAIR SHIRTS, HAIR PANTS** AND **HAIR TIES!**

MAJOR – WHEN YOU HAVE A MOMENT I'D LIKE A **QUIET WORD!**

I **SLUM IT** HALFWAY ROUND THE WORLD ON A MISSION OF GOODWILL AND RECONCILIATION...

...AND I GET A FACEFUL OF **ANTIPODEAN ARSE** EVERYWHERE I STEP, LARGELY THANKS TO YOUR **LOVE-IN** WITH MONSIEUR CHIRAC LAST WEEK. TELL ME, DO YOU EVER THINK MORE THAN **THREE MINUTES** AHEAD, MAJOR?

THREE MINUTES IS A **LONG** TIME IN POLITICS, MAJESTY!

BOOM BOOM BOOM

– 6·11·3696 –

©Steve Bell '95

36

37

OFTOS THE OFFICE FOR TAKING OUT SCHOOLS

LOOK AT THIS, SPOTTY

ROWF!

I'VE JUST WRITTEN A NOVEL THAT PROVES: Ⓐ: TEACHERS ARE A LOAD OF DONKEYS Ⓑ: THEY CAN'T COUNT;

ARF!

Ⓒ: THEY GOT NOMORALS Ⓓ: THEY CAN'T SPEAK PROPER; AND Ⓔ: THERE'S TOO MANY OF 'EM!

WOOF!

WHO'S PULLING YOUR STRINGS? ARF?

SHUT YOUR MOUTH!!

13·11·37·01~   © Steve Bell '95.

THE MAN FROM OFTOS

I'M BAD AND I'M SAD!!

·14·11·37·02~

ONLY TWENTY NINE KIDS? YOU COULD GET AT LEAST **SEVENTY** IN HERE!

© Steve Bell 1995~

SPOTTY — GO RUSTLE ME UP ANOTHER **FORTY ONE** KIDS!

ARF!

NOW **SPOTTY'S** GONNA TEACH YOU THE **THREE 'R's** IN LESS TIME THAN IT TAKES ME TO GET A **BAD HAIRCUT**!

RRRR!

SEE YOU LATER!

THE MAN FROM OFTOS

THE OFFICE FOR TAKING OUT SCHOOLS

THE THREE 'R's by Spotty Dog

RUFF!

RUFF!   RUFF!   RUFF!

·15·11·37·03~

© Steve Bell 1995~

ROWF!

ROWF!   ROWF!   ROWF!

RRRRRRR!

RRRRR!   RRRRR!   RRRRR!

RUFF! ROWF! RRRRR! RUFF! ROWF! RRRR!

RUFF! ROWF! RRRRR!!

THERE YOU ARE! SCIENTIFIC PROOF THAT SCHOOLS **DON'T** NEED **EXTRA** RESOURCES!

THE MAN FROM OFTOS GOES TO ETON

·16·11·37·04~

© Steve Bell '95~

DON'T WALK **THAH**, YOU SHAGGING **OIK**!

YOU CAN AINLY WALK **THAH** IF YOU'VE BEEN BUGGERED BY **HEAD OF HICE**...... WHO ARE YOU ANYWAY?

I'M HEAD OF THE **SCHOOLS INSPECTION SERVICE**

...I'VE HEARD THAT CLASSES HERE MAY BE **TOO SMALL**

OH DO SHAG ORFF!! YOU'RE AN **OIK**!! WE INSPECT YOU!!

38

THE MAN FROM OFTOS GOES TO ETON

SORRY OLD BEAN — 'FRAID YOUR **WRIT** DOESN'T RUN HERE.....

BUT I HAD MY HAIRCUT SPECIALLY!

...WE'RE ALREADY SO SUPERB AS TO BE BEYOND SUPERBNESS...

TELL YOU WHAT — IF YOU WANT TO MAKE YOURSELF USEFUL.... ...WARM UP THIS **LATIN PRIMER** FOR THE PRINCE...

...I CAN SEE YOU'VE GOT A **FIRST CLASS BRAIN** — IT SHOWS IN THE **HAIRCUT,** Y'KNOW....

HOW DO I WARM IT UP??

STUFF IT DINE YOUR TRIZERS OF COURSE, MAN! ONLY THE BEST FOR OUR **FUTURE MONARCH!**

BRILLIANT PARTY, 'ARRY!

CONGRATULATIONS ON GETTING YOUR **BUS PASS,** LARRY BOY!

PSSSHHT! 'ARRY!!

COURSE I'M **PISSHED!** IT'S MY BIRTHDAY! — WHAT D'YOU WANT BARRY?

NAH! I MEAN "PSSSHHT — I'M GONNA WHISPER IN YER EAR"..... D'YOU FANCY A **TWIGLET?**

NO THANKS — NEVER TOUCH 'EM!

GARN... **'AVE A TWIGLET!**

I DON'T LIKE TWIGLETS.... ...I DON'T USE 'EM, BARRY!

...YOU'LL FEEL **BETTER** AFTER YOU'VE **HAD A SNACK,** 'ARRY!

WELL...

SINCE YOU PUT IT LIKE THAT... **I DO LIKE A SNACK,** ME

PRETTY **NICE,** EH 'ARRY?.... 'ARRY??.... 'ARRY? YOU **ALL RIGHT!**

AWWWGGKKK!! QUICK! FETCH A PHOTOGRAPHER!

BLOODY 'ELL! ONE BAD **TWIGLET** AND 'E'S TURNED INTO A **VEGETABLE!**

'ARRY?

WHEZZHA PHOTOGRAPHER?

THE PHOTOGRAPHER'S ON HIS WAY, 'ARRY DARLIN'! **WHAT** DID YOU JUST GIVE 'IM, BLOCKHEAD!

IT WAS A **TWIGLET!** IT WAS JUST A **BIT OF A SNACK,** YOU KNOW.... WHERE'D YOU GET IT FROM? SAINSBURYS I THINK...

SAY "CHEESE" HARRY

SNACKS ARE EVIL!

39

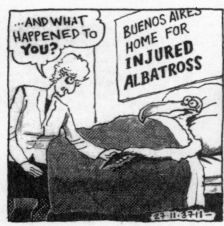

40

41

42

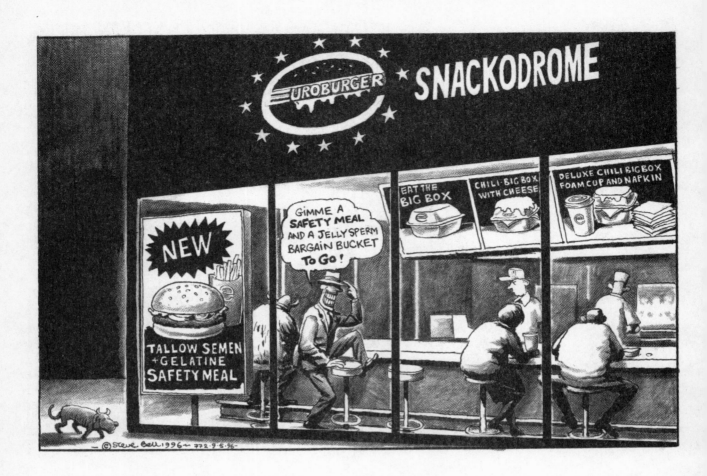

44

48

WE WILL END OUR OPT OUT FROM THE SOCIAL CHAPTER OF THE SINGLE EUROPEAN FEAST.....

...WE WILL RESTORE THROUGH TICKETING ON ALL TURKEY CRATES...

THANKS TO BRIAN

...AND WE WILL REFORM THE HOUSE OF MATTHEWS!!

SPIN

COLLEAGUES-I BELIEVE IN OUR FUTURE WITH A FERVOUR YOU CAN ONLY GUESS AT — JUST LOOK AT MY EYEBALLS!

...THAT'S WHY I'VE SENT MY BOY TO COOKERY SCHOOL AND ACCEPTED AN INVITATION TO SANDRINGHAM!!

FAMILY, NOBS, SWELLS, ARMY, CHURCH + MEDIA ← THIS WAY

SERVANTS

PHEASANTS AND TURKEYS

© Steve Bell 1995

CASUALTY LITE

DR DA DA DA BUM BUM BAAA DA DA DA BUM BUM BAAA...

AMBULANCE

GOT A BLEEDER.... GIVEN HIM 34 MS OF PLJ AND FOUR ECTs AT NINETEEN AND ELEVEN....

VIRTUAL MEDIC

HOW MANY FINGERS AM I HOLDING UP? I'M GOING TO HAVE TO CUT HIS PANTS OFF, CHARLEY...

I WANT A DCM ON A BLT. SIR! CAN YOU HEAR ME? HOW ARE YOU FEELING?

FIT AS A FIDDLE AND TWICE AS NORMAL!

LITE CASUALTY

16·1·3732

I CAN'T FIND A PULSE - I THINK HE'S NHS!

CAN YOU STOP TALKING IN CODE, FOR CHRISSAKE! NHS -NO HOPE SUNBEAM - SHOVE HIM BEHIND SOME CURTAINS..

...WE GOTTA PRIORITISE! HERE'S A FAMILY OF SQUASHED HEDGEHOGS OFF THE M25 — IT'S CARNAGE OUT THERE...

STAND BACK!

©Steve Bell '95

50

52

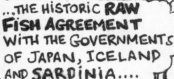

SOCKS — THE 'STATE OF MY BASKET' SPEECH

THIS YEAR I SIGNED....

...THE HISTORIC RAW FISH AGREEMENT WITH THE GOVERNMENTS OF JAPAN, ICELAND AND SARDINIA....

...I HAVE ENGINEERED COMPREHENSIVE 'LAND FOR FISH' DEALS IN BOSNIA, NORTHERN IRELAND AND THE ISRAELI-OCCUPIED WEST BANK...

...AND I HAVE PERFORMED ALL THIS THROUGH THE EYE OF AN ELEPHANT'S ASS!!!

I LIKE THE FORWARD-LOOKING LIGHT SUIT, IAN. IT'S GOOD TO BE SEEN TO GET MODERN!

THAT'S WHY I'M SO IMPRESSED BY THIS NEW SMALL-SCALE ROCKET TECHNOLOGY...

SUGAR POWERED ROCKET TRIUMPH

...JUST IMAGINE, IAN — A PROTESTANT DETERRENT FOR A PROTESTANT PEOPLE!

WHEN ARE YOU BUMS GONNA GET ROUND A TABLE? WE'RE GETTIN' BORED OVER HERE!

SEE HERE POOSSY — WE WILL NEVORR SIT DOYN WITH THOSE WHO SIT DOYN WITH... (ETC.)

NO TALKS WITHOUT SURRENDORR, NO SURRENDORR WITHOUT TALKS, NO TALKS WITHOUT ELECTIONS... ...(ETC. ETC...)

LISTEN... CAN'T YOU DO IT ALL, LIKE, SIMULTANEOUSLY? THE WHOLE THING'S STARTING TO FALL APART!

IAN! I'VE JUST HAD A FABULOUS IDEA!

I'VE JUST BEEN WATCHING THE FILLUM 'SUPERMAN' — Y'KNOW WHERE THE MAN OF STEEL WHIZZES ROUND THE WORLD SEVERAL TIMES...

...AND TURNS THE CLOCK BACK TO BRING LOIS LANE BACK TO LIFE.....

...I THOUGHT THAT, BY UTILISING OUR ALL-NEW SWEET TEA AND FRIED BREAD-POWERED PROTESTANT DETERRENT...

...WE COULD DO EXACTLY THE SAME THING IN REVERSE! WE COULD HAVE TALKS WITH SINN FEIN/IRA WITHOUT ALTERING OUR POSITION BUT BY SIMPLY DISTORTING THE SPACE/TIME CONTINUUM!

YER TWISTIN' MY HEID!!

53

54

55

60

61

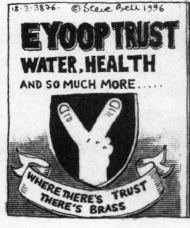

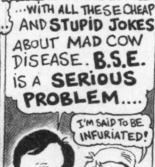

68

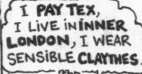

73

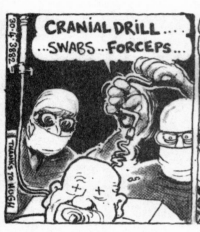

75

76

THE PIES ARE ANGRY - 9·5·3909 -

HEY – YOU KNOW WE HAVE TO LIST ALL THE INGREDIENTS IN FOOD PRODUCTS LIKE THIS FINE-LOOKING PIE??

YES?

WELL... HOW COME WE DON'T HAVE TO DO THE SAME THING...

CONTAINS MEATY SUBSTANCES, GRAVY, CRUSTY BITS, HYDROGENISED FEELGOOD FACTOR E102349682291/x::

...FOR ANIMAL FEEDS?

BECAUSE COWS CAN'T READ, FOOL!

PELLETED MOOSNAX

CONTAINS: NONE OF YOUR BUSINESS

THE PIES ARE ANGRY - 10·5·3910 -

YOU'RE PULLING MY PLONKER! YOU'RE SERIOUSLY TELLING ME WE DON'T LIST THE INGREDIENTS ON ANIMAL FEED PACKAGING BECAUSE COWS CAN'T READ?

YOU CALLING ME A LIAR?

MOOSNAX

LOOK – LET'S NOT BEAT ABOUT THE BUSH – COME ON – ADMIT IT – YOU'RE WORRIED ABOUT THIS 'ROGUE PROTEIN' THAT MAY CAUSE BSE/CJD AREN'T YOU?

WELL.... ...I SUPPOSE

...SO WHAT GOOD IS LABELLING FEEDBAGS "CHICKENSHIT, EGGBOX + SHEEP-BRAIN-PUS" GOING TO DO? IT'LL JUST WORRY THE POOR DOOMED COWS!

OUCH! I THINK THIS PIE JUST BIT ME!!

78

SHIRLEY PORTER THE MILLIONAIRE'S DAUGHTER

THERE IS NOTHING LIKE A DAME....

...AND YOU ARE NOTHING LIKE A DAME. DAMES DON'T GET CAUGHT!!

CRUMP

© Steve Bell 1996

BLINKING FLIP!

SID?

GAS SHARES TAKE TUMBLE

SID

CRIKEY, ALEXIS — THIS IS THE GREATEST SMASH AND GRAB RAID OF ALL TIME!

WHAT'S THE PROBLEM, SMALL TIMER?

...AND NOW THE CHAIRMAN OF BRITISH GAS WANTS TO UNLOAD SMALL SHAREHOLDERS BECAUSE WE'RE TOO EXPENSIVE TO SERVICE! GOODBYE CRUEL WORLD!!

WOULD IT HELP IF I MASS-AGED YOUR BUTTOCKS WITH MY FOOT?

© Steve Bell 1996

LOOK — I'VE FILLED IN MY APPLICATION FORM FOR THE RAILTRACK FREE MONEY OFFER!

GEED MORNEENG!

SHARE SHACK

I'VE SIGNED IT AT THE BOTTOM WITH MY OWN NAME...

GEED MORNEENG SID! HAVE YOU READ THE SMALL PRINT?

NO..

SID

NOW I'M OFF HOME TO WAIT FOR THE DIVIDENDS TO CASCADE THROUGH MY LETTERBOX!

GEED MORN-EEENG!

SHARE SHACK

© Steve Bell '96

LET'S SEE — I COULD HAVE MADE ANYTHING UP TO £150 ON MY RAILTRACK SHAREDEALINGS!

SO THAT'S £150, LESS FEES, LESS COMMISSION, LESS TEN DAYS WAGES IN LIEU OF QUEUING AND ADMIN. TIME; THAT MEANS AT LAST I CAN AFFORD...

...THAT HOLIDAY IN THE HINDU KUSH I'VE BEEN PROMISING MYSELF, PROVIDING I CAN DISGUISE MYSELF AS A GOAT FOR LIVE EXPORT.....

© Steve Bell 1996

80

86

WE'RE GETTING PISSED WE'RE GETTING PISSED WE'RE GETTING..

PISSBALL'S GETTING WET....

...THREE SHIRTS ON YOUR LION CHINA RIM STILL GLEAMING THIRTY BEERS A TIME TEND TO MAKE YOU STEAMING..

YOU'RE MY LAST HOPE, URI – MAKE ME POPULAR WITH THE AID OF YOUR AMAZING POWERS!

READING FOR THE CUP DROP

OOOOH!! I CAN FEEL A WEIRD TINGLING SENSATION!...

– © Steve Bell '96

YOU'VE MADE MY GLASSES FALL OFF! THAT REALLY IS STUPENDOUS!!

READING FOR THE CUP DROP

YES – WE'VE DEFINITELY GOT TO DO SOMETHING!

Colour me BOLLOCKS
IMAGE CONSULTANTS

19·6·3933

WE'LL TRY YOU ON OUR 'SUCCESS BY ASSOCIATION' PACKAGE...

STUFF THIS PILLOW DOWN THE FRONT OF YOUR UNDERPANTS, LEAN OVER BACKWARDS...A BIT OF HAIR DYE AND YOU ARE WAYWARD GENIUS GAZZA-MAZZA!

© Steve Bell 1996

YEEOOOOOOW GEORMAN BASSTAD...

FABULOUS – YOU MOVE WELL!

20·6·3934

YEE TAKIN A PISS OOT WOR BEEF??

© Steve Bell '96

FOOK RIGHT OFF NOO WORRALL KICK YOUR TELLY IN!!

87

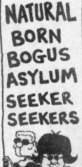

THE ROAD TO MANI FESTO WITH BOB, BING + DOROTHY

- SAY **DOLL** — WHADDYA THINK OF MY **TURQUOISE PORRIDGE**?
- HMMM — TASTES KINDA TURQUOISE
- CAN I **CONFIDE** IN YOU, **BOB**?
- SURE THING, **DOROTHY**!
- I'M **IN LOVE WITH BING** AND I'M GOING TO **HAVE HIS BABY**!
- WHY THAT'S **WONDERFUL NEWS**, **DOROTHY**!! WHEN'S THE BABY DUE?
- ANY DAY NOW, **BOB**!!
- IS EVERYTHING READY FOR YOU TO GO INTO **NEW LABOUR**?
- **YOU BET, BOB! I CAN'T WAIT!**

THE ROAD TO MANI FESTO WITH BING BOB + DOROTHY

- BIG SUITS, WARM WORDS AND **YOOOOOU** ... ♪
- ... I NEVER WILL BE **BLOOOOOO** ...
- ... I'VE FOUND ANOTHER HUE BECAUSE **I'M TURQUOISE** ♪ BA-DOOBY-DOOBY-DOOBY DOO-SNAT-SNAT-SNAT

THE ROAD TO MANI FESTO WITH BING BOB + DOROTHY

- MY BABY'S GONE INTO **NEW LABOUR** ♪ I GAVE THE **NEW** MIDWIFE A CALL ...
- ... SHE SAID **NOT TO WORRY** THERE'S NO NEED TO **HURRY** NEW LABOUR'S LIKE **HAVING A BALL** ...
- NWNNGH
- ... **NO PAIN**, NO MESS AND NO DISCORD NO **UNPLEASANT** BODILY SLIME
- GGGGGMMMFF
- **IT ISN'T A COP OUT** ♪ THOSE BLAIR BABES WILL **POP OUT** TIME AFTER TIME **AFTER TIME!**

- © Steve Bell 1996 -

- HUMPHREY! HUMPHREY?
- COME AND HAVE A DELICIOUS PLATE OF ALL-NEW ALL-SAFE **GUMMERBRAINS**®-™-
- CATS LOVE GUMMER BRAINS
- **GROUND UP GREY MATTER** IN **GREASY GREEN GRAVY** — YOU'LL LOVE 'EM!
- HUMPHREY? COOO-EEE!!!

15.7.3946 -

90

91

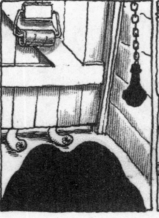

93

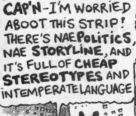

94

95

BRING YOUR NOTEBOOK, TISHA — I WANNA DICTATE AN EDITORIAL....

SIR HAROLD HARDNOSE

4·9·3963

"FEELGOOD FACTOR ISH BACK, DEFINITELY FEEL A BUZZ..." BRRARRP!

© Steve Bell 1996 —

"...I REMBMBER...WINTERDISHCONTENT, SHTREESH FULLA UN-BURIED SHTIFFS, SHABBY SHOCIALIST SHUPERSHTATE...."

HOW DO YOU SPELL 'BRRARRP'?

IT DOESHN'T MARRER....YOU FILL IN DETAILSH.... CUT! PRINT! IT'SH A WRAP!!

I FEEL ANOTHER ONE COMIN' ON...

5·9·3964

TISHA! BRING YER NOTEBOOK...

BEEEEEP

© Steve Bell 1996 —

"YOUNG PEOPLE TODAY...NO SHTANDARDSH, NO RESHPECT, NO ORDER..."

"SHMACK'EM INNA FACE! INSHTIL QUIET, ORDERLINESSH AND ACCEPTANCE OF AUTHORITY!"

YOU FILL IN DETAILSH... CUT! PRINT! IT'SH A WRAP!!

I THINK I'VE SHAT MESELF!

I DON'T WANT EIGHTIES STUFF....

6·9·3965

LUCAN HARDNOSE
LIFESTYLE CORRESPONDENT

...I WANT TO KNOW WHAT THEY'RE WEARING IN THE REFUGEE CAMPS IN ZAIRE....

WHY AM I SURROUNDED BY TOSSERS?!? WHO'S THIS ON LINE 2?

SHA KLUNK

TISHA! WHAT CAN I D... YOUR FATHER'S HAD AN ACCIDENT, LUCAN!

© Steve Bell 1996 —

9·9·3966 —

LORD PARCHMENT— YOU SERVED IN THREE POST-WAR CABINETS...

© Steve Bell 1996 —

...AND WERE CHAIRMAN OF FOURTEEN OF THE NATION'S MOST SUCCESSFUL COMPANIES...

...DO YOU WANT ME TO CRUSH YOUR HEAD BETWEEN MY ENORMOUS THIGHS??

BY GOLLY YOU'RE A HEALTHY GIRL, MISS HARDNOSE!

...WHAT IS IT, LUCAN? —IT HAD BETTER BE SOMETHING IMPORTANT!

DADDY'S HAD AN ACCIDENT?? WELL I WANT HIS BLOODY CAR!!

COME TO THINK OF IT I'LL HAVE HIS JOB TOO! WHERE DID IT HAPPEN? —UNDERNEATH HIS DESK?!!??

IN THAT CASE I'M DEFINITELY GOING TO NEED A NEW CARPET!!

© Steve Bell 1996

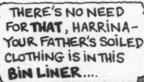

THIS IS A SAD DAY FOR ME, TISHA...... CAN I GO IN AND PAY MY LAST RESPECTS?

THERE'S NO NEED FOR THAT, HARRINA— YOUR FATHER'S SOILED CLOTHING IS IN THIS BIN LINER....

...HIS CAR KEYS, WATCH AND CREDIT CARDS ARE IN THIS JIFFY BAG....

THANKS!

...AND YOUR FATHER IS PROPPED UP IN THE EXECUTIVE WASHROOM.... ...MISS HARDNOSE? HARRINA!! SLAM ..OH!

LORD FOODSTUFF—YOU'VE BEEN CHAIRMAN OF THE MULE GROUP FOR TWO DYNAMIC YEARS AND I HAVE JUST ONE WORD I'D LIKE YOU TO HEAR...

"CONTINUITY"!! ONLY A HARDNOSE CAN PICK UP WHERE A HARDNOSE LEFT OFF!

THIS ISN'T NEPOTISM, THIS IS THE FORWARD MARCH OF GO-GETTER GENES!! START TOMORROW... ...AND DON'T FORGET TO BRING THOSE THIGHS!!

© Steve Bell 1996

WE'LL GET RID OF THOSE PICTURES, AND GET RID OF YOURSELF WHILE YOU'RE ABOUT IT!

I WANT THE EXECUTIVE WASHROOM DONE OUT IN FLAME TURQUOISE!

DADDY!! YOU'RE ALIVE! FACTS WRONG TO THE LAST! YOU'RE FIRED!!

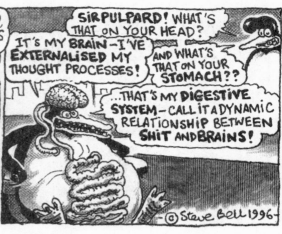

101

NORMA! NORMA!! I'VE JUST DONE SOME-THING **ENORMOUSLY SIGNIFICANT!**

20·9·3975

I'VE JUST NAMED A STAR "**PLANET NEWSCORP MOTHERCARE**"!

OH JOHN, YOU'RE SO **THOUGHTFUL** – HOW DID YOU MANAGE THAT?

THERE WAS THIS FELLOW IN TRAFALGAR SQUARE. – I PAID HIM **GOOD MONEY!**

...HE SOLD ME **NELSON'S COLUMN** AS WELL!

– © STEVE BELL '96 –

23·9·3976

YOU CAN **RUN**, BISHOP NOJOHNNIES, BUT YOU **CAN'T HIDE!!**

© Steve Bell 1996

I AM **THE LORD THY GOD** AND I WILL **FIND YOU OUT** WHEREVER YOU MAY BE!

...AND YOU WILL **GIVE ME YOUR ADDRESS BOOK** AND THE NAME OF **YOUR AGENT!**

PSSST!...DARLING!

24·9·3977

...WHEN THIS ALL **BLOWS OVER**, WILL YOU **MARRY ME?**

I DON'T WANT **SEX**, I DON'T WANT **MONEY**, I DON'T WANT **EXCITEMENT**; I JUST WANT TO LIVE LIKE ANY OTHER **NORMAL CATHOLIC COUPLE**

-- © Steve Bell 1996 –

THEY SAY GUILT IS A **BIG CATHOLIC THING**, BUT I DON'T FEEL GUILT...

© Steve Bell '96

25·9·3978

...I FEEL **GOOD** ABOUT US, ABOUT WHAT WE ARE AND WHAT WE DID.... ...OF COURSE I REGRET ANY PAIN I CAUSED THAT **SHEEP DOG**....

IT'S **OVER**, BISHOP RICK NOJOHNNIES! I'M **LEAVING YOU!**

WAIT! WHAT WE HAD WAS **PURE** AND...

AÏEEEE!!

BAM

THE NIGEL LAWSON DIET PLAN

① DESTROY ECONOMY

② DRINK CLARET

③ **** OFF

④ DIE

© Steve Bell 1996

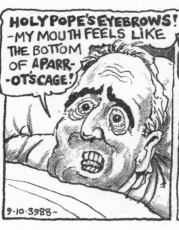

HOLY POPE'S EYEBROWS! — MY MOUTH FEELS LIKE THE BOTTOM OF A PARR-OT'S CAGE!

WHAT A SPEECH! WHAT A TRIUMPH!! WHAT A NIGHT!

BUT, BY GOD — MY ARM'S STIFF... ...I MUST HAVE PULLED!! OOOOHH...

...NOOOOOOO!! ZZZZZZ OOOOMMMM ZZZZZZZ

OH NO!! I'VE WOKEN UP IN BED WITH A MAD COW LYING ON MY ARM!

OOOMMM ZZZZZ

HOW AM I GOING TO GET OUT OF THIS WITHOUT WAKING IT UP?

I SUPPOSE I COULD BE LIKE A COYOTE AND CHEW MY OWN ARM OFF....

...EXCEPT I WOULDN'T WANT TO RISK GETTING MAWHINNEY MOLECULES INTO MY FOOD CHAIN!

© Steve Bell 1996

HEY PEOPLE — -I WANT YOU TO PUT YOUR HANDS TOGETHER!...

...AND GIVE A BIG WARM TORY WELCOME TO THE MAN WITH THE BIG HEART AND THE BIG PANTS!

YEE HAA!

EEEEK EEEK!

THE MAN WE ALL KNOW, LOVE AND TRUST..... HE'S NO HYPOCRITE, HE'S A WINNER...

...HE'S THE WINNER OF THE EUROVISION SLEAZE CONTEST — LONG JOHN MAJOR!

© Steve Bell 1996

105

106

Conservative Policy on BSE 1990-1996:

— 873·18·12·96 —

— © Steve Bell 1996 —

— THE WOMAN WHO SUGGESTED ACTUALLY CLEANING THE SHIT OFF THE MEAT — APOLOGIES TO HM BATEMAN   © Steve Bell 1997

111

112

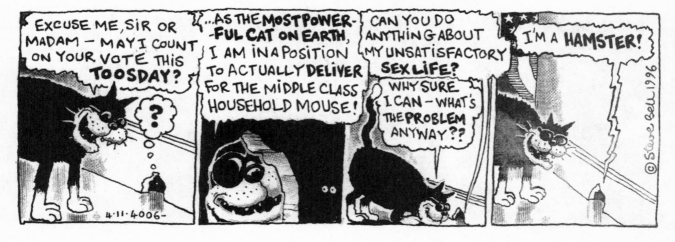

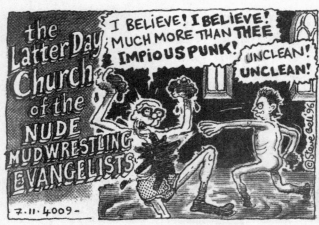

114

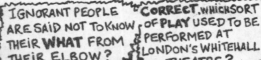
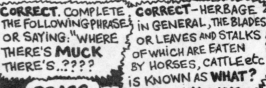

MASTER MIND

with DEEP SHEEP

IGNORANT PEOPLE ARE SAID NOT TO KNOW THEIR **WHAT** FROM THEIR ELBOW?

ARSE

CORRECT. WHICH SORT OF **PLAY** USED TO BE PERFORMED AT LONDON'S WHITEHALL THEATRE?

FARCE

CORRECT. COMPLETE THE FOLLOWING PHRASE OR SAYING: "WHERE THERE'S **MUCK** THERE'S..????

BRASS

CORRECT—HERBAGE IN GENERAL, THE BLADES OR LEAVES AND STALKS OF WHICH ARE EATEN BY HORSES, CATTLE etc. IS KNOWN AS **WHAT**?

PASS

I'M SORRY—THE ANSWER WAS "**GRASS**" AND AT THE END OF THAT ROUND YOU HAVE SCORED THREE POINTS

© Steve Bell '96

POLICE

SMART MONKEY WANTED
EASY WORK NO HEAVY LIFTING

© Steve Bell 1996

?

ELLO ELLO

SMART MONKEY WANTED
EASY WORK NO HEAVY LIFTING

'ELLO **JOHN**, MY LITTLE PAL!

BADGER!

WHAT'S ALL THIS ABOUT A '**SMART MONKEY**'? YOU WANT SOMEONE TO GO ROUND COLLECTING YOUR **BRIBES** AGAIN?

NAH, NAH—THIS IS TOTALLY **LEGIT**! HOME OFFICE FUNDED PROJECT!

DECORATING YOUR HOUSE?

HO HO HO! YOU'RE A **CYNICAL** LITTLE DEVIL AND NO MISTAKE! NO, NO—WE JUST WANT YOU TO **TEST DRIVE** THIS ELEC-TRONIC TAGGING DEVICE

AND ALL THE BANANAS I CAN EAT, RIGHT?

© Steve Bell '96

REGENT'S PARK DISCO NITE SPOT

'OW OLD ARE YOU, MOOSH?

I'M **SEVENTEEN**—THAT'S THREE HUNDRED AND FIVE IN MONKEY YEARS. HAVE A **BANANA**!

NNNK

I'M GONNA **STAY UP LATE** AND DRINK DAIQUIRIS!

✱ **OLLOCKS**! I FORGOT ABOUT THE **ELECTRONIC TAG**!

NNTIN NZZZT

© Steve Bell '96

116

117

120

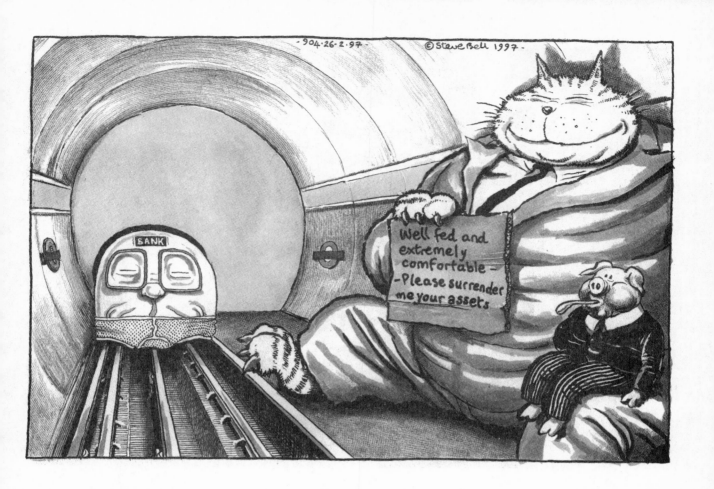

LAME DUCK PRIME MINISTER

LAME DICK PRESIDENT

HOLDING ON TILL MAYDAY

HOLDING ON TILL MAYDAY WITH CHINESE CHARACTERISTICS

124

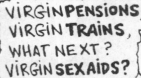

Tell Sid there's quids in kids on the skids

— 23·1·4047 —

British Socserve — THE CARING SELL-OFF

PLEASE SON — — CAN I HAVE SOME MORE?

© Steve Bell '97

REASONS TO BE CYNICAL

— PART ONE —

— 27·1·4048 —

KENSINGTON & CHELSEA CONSERVATIVE ASSOCIATION

MR CLARK — IN A BLAZE OF MORAL RECTITUDE WE'VE JUST GOT RID OF ONE ALLEGED OLD DRUNK...

... WHAT MAKES YOU THINK WE WANT AN **EVEN OLDER** SHAGGER AS OUR PROSPECTIVE CANDIDATE ??

BECAUSE I AM A WEALTHY AND DISINTERESTED OLD SHAGGER WHO IS BARKINGLY **RIGHT WING!**

BUT, DAMMIT, YOU'RE A SHAGGER THAT **OPPOSES HUNTING!**

I NO LONGER OPPOSE HUNTING BECAUSE: "KENSINGTON ET CHELSEA VAUT UN RENARD MORT!"

BRAVO! MINE'S A STIFF ONE!

© Steve Bell 1997

REASONS TO BE CYNICAL

PART 2

28·1·4049

ALAN — YOU'VE BETRAYED ME ONCE **TOO OFTEN** — I'M LEAVING YOU!

DON'T WALK AWAY, RENÉ! ALL THIS TOSH ABOUT ANIMAL RIGHTS —

LET'S FACE IT — YOU'D SHAG **ANYTHING** — ME, YOUR CONSCIENCE, **THAT WARDROBE,** IN YOUR BID TO GET YOUR GRUBBY LITTLE MITTS NEAR THE **LEVERS OF POWER!**

I'D NEVER SHAG THAT WARDROBE — IT'S INHERITED!

© Steve Bell 1996

REASONS TO BE CYNICAL

PART 3

PHOTOCALL WITH **GUMMER** AND **MAJOR!** LIFE AS A CANDIDATE IS HOTTING UP

A PHOTO-OPPORTUNITY TO BE SEEN WITH TWO OF THE PEOPLE I MOST **ADMIRE** IN THE ENTIRE KINGDOM... **NOT!!**

CHUCKLE SNORT!

MMMM — **FOXBURGER!** THE SAFE ALTERNATIVE TO RUSSIAN ROULETTE!!

MMMNNGGH

© Steve Bell 1997

29·1·4050

128

130

131

ONE MAN'S DOG IS ANOTHER MAN'S POISSON

MARKET BOY — TURN INTO A FISH!

TURN INTO FISH PASTE!

NOW — JUMP INTO THIS SANDWICH!

WHEEE SLASH SLASH

THAT'S NOT DRIFT AND UNCERTAINTY — THAT'S LEADERSHIP!

GOOD AFTERNOON OFFICER

I ALREADY KNOW THAT

WE KNOW YOU'RE INTENDING TO CROSS THE ROAD. WE EVEN KNOW WHO YOUR ACCOMPLICES ARE. THE POLICE KNOW, Y'KNOW.

YOU FARTED BADGER?

YOU MEAN YOU FARTED, JOHN

I DIDN'T FART! WE ALREADY KNOW YOU FARTED.

I DIDN'T @*!!@* FART, YOU *!!☆*! @*!!*! ☆*!@*

DON'T WASTE YOUR BREATH. THE POLICE KNOW, Y'KNOW

BANG

BANG

Madame Badger

KNOWS YOUR INNERMOST THOUGHTS

YOU'VE GOT SOMETHING ON YOUR MIND — GIVE ME AN ITEM OF YOUR CLOTHING

THIS SOCK'S BEEN INVOLVED IN AN ARMED ROBBERY

LOOK — THERE'S A CANARY IN THE SOCK — SAYS YOU KILLED COCK ROBIN

133

THE WARM WEATHER PAYMENT

Panel 1: LET'S PUT OUR **STOMACHS** ON **THE TABLE**, CHIEF CONSTABLE

Panel 2: THAT SOCK — IT WON'T **WASH**, Y'KNOW. THAT CANARY'S **WHISTLING IN THE DARK**...

Panel 3: WHAT **MOTIVATES** YOU, CHIEF CONSTABLE? SHALL I TELL YOU WHAT MOTIVATES YOU, **IN ONE WORD**?

Panel 4: **MONKEYS**, CHIEF CONSTABLE. PURE, UNADULTER-ATED **LUST FOR MONKEYS**!

— © Steve Bell 1997

Panel 1: THAT PSYCHOLOGIST GEEZER REALLY **SORTED ME OUT**, JOHN

Panel 2: MY FITTING PEOPLE UP ALL THE TIME WAS JUST A **CRY FOR HELP**. I KNOW WHAT I **REALLY WANT** NOW.

Panel 3: I WANT TO **CHANGE SEX, GROW HAIR** ALL OVER MY BODY AND HAVE **YOUR BABIES** USING NEW CLONING TECH-NOLOGY

Panel 4: THEN I'LL THINK ABOUT **GOING STRAIGHT!**

© Steve Bell '97

Panel 1: DID YOU KNOW THEY'VE SUCCESSFULLY ISOLATED THE **GENE** RESPONSIBLE FOR **NEW LABOUR**?

Panel 2: YOU'RE TALKING OUT OF YOUR ARSE

Panel 3: WRONG — **I'M** TALKING OUT OF YOUR ARSE

Panel 4: **YOU'RE** TALKING OUT OF **MY** ARSE!

© Steve Bell 1997

Panel 1: DID YOU KNOW THEY'VE SUCCESSFULLY ISOLATED THE **GENE** RESPONSIBLE FOR **NEW LABOUR** AND CLONED IT ONTO A SHEEP'S BACKSIDE?

Panel 2: I KNOW! OH NO!

Panel 3: I KNOW SOMETHING ELSE. WHAT'S THAT?

Panel 4: BRITISH SCIENTISTS HAVE DEVELOPED **CONTENT-FREE UNDERPANTS**!

© Steve Bell 1997

— THANKS TO BRIAN —

137

MORE QUERIES HERE: Ms. W. OF STREATHAM WANTS TO KNOW WHY WE'VE SWAPPED PLACES WITH 'DOONESBURY'

11·3·4079

IT'S A LONGSTORY BUT BASICALLY IT INVOLVES VIOLENCE KIDNAPPING AND BAD LANGUAGE...

© Steve Bell 1997

TELL US WHY YOU WEAR YOUR GLASSES UNDER YOUR NOSE!

SMACK HIM AGAIN!

MR H. OF BIRMINGHAM WANTS TO KNOW WHEN WE'RE GOING TO CLEAN UP OUR PANEL BORDERS AND USE MECHANICAL TONE

NEVER!

S. BAG OF TOTTENHAM ASKS: DO YOU EVER RUN OUT OF IDEAS?

12·3·4080

NNNG NNNG

HYDROGENATED FISH OIL

SLURK SLURK SLURK

© Steve Bell 1997

AAAAAHH!

WHAT WAS THAT?

J.R. OF DALLAS WANTS TO KNOW WHY THERE AREN'T MORE WOMEN IN THIS STRIP?

13·3·4081

I SHOWED THIS LETTER TO THE ARTIST, AND HE FAINTED. WHEN HE CAME TO, HE THOUGHT FOR A MOMENT......

...THEN HE LOOKED ME IN THE EYE AND SAID: "BECAUSE WHEN YOU'VE HAD MARGARET THATCHER IN YOUR STRIP..."

"...EVERYTHING ELSE PALES INTO INSIGNIFICANCE" ...AND THEN HE FAINTED AGAIN

© Steve Bell 1997

R.A. OF EXETER WRITES: "WHY DO ALL THE CHARACTERS IN YOUR STRIP LACK PSYCHOLOGICAL DEPTH?"

14·3·4082

THAT'S EASY!!

YOU SEE — WE'RE NOT 'CHARACTERS' — WE NEVER HAVE BEEN. WE ARE SQUIGGLY LINES WITH ATTITUDE!

© Steve Bell 97

WE ARE CARTOON CHARACTERS. WE ARE CIPHERS. SOME CIPHERS DEPLOY PSYCHOLOGICAL NATURALISM — RIGHT MIKE? WHY UNDER THE NOSE? WHY?

SOME CIPHERS DEPLORE PSYCHOLOGICAL NATURALISM.

YOU WON'T TELL ME — YOU DIE!

DON'T WORRY. WE LOVE 'DOONESBURY'

OUR **FALKLANDS RELATIVES** ARE COMING OVER AGAIN....

"IN THIS **HOUR OF NEED** FOR THE CONSERVATIVE PARTY, LOYAL FALKLANDS PENGUINRY ARE COMING...

...TO JOIN THE FIGHT TO PRESERVE THE PARTY THEY LOVE." THEY'R ARRIVING TONIGHT AND THEY WANT US TO LAY ON A **BIG FISH DINNER!**

SO THAT'S FUCKWIT, NAZI, FASCIST, SPANKER, FUCKWIT, NAZI, FASCIST, SPANKER.....

THANKS TO THE WINDMILL BOYS

THE **QUEEN**
THE **QUEEN**
THE **QUEEN**
THE **QUEEN**

THAT REMINDS ME: I LAY THE PROBLEMS OF SOCIETY TODAY AT THE FOOT OF **GAY SEALS!**

YEAH!

YEAH!

THOSE SLIPPERY **BARKING POOFS** WITH THEIR SPIKY MOUSTACHES...

...CLAPPING THEIR **LIMP FLIPPERS** AND BALANCING BEACHBALLS ON THEIR SLIMY NOSES!

MAKES ME SHUDDER!

WE MUST MAKE **ALBATROSS** AN ELECTION ISSUE!

THERE'S BEEN A **CONSPIRACY OF SILENCE** ABOUT ALBATROSS...

THEY COME OVER HERE WITH THEIR **BIG FEET** AND THEIR **MASSIVE WINGSPANS**...

...BY **ALL** THE MAJOR PARTIES!

THEY GLIDE AROUND IN **THERMALS** ALL DAY... ...SHOWING OF THEIR **MASSIVE WINGSPANS!**

THEY NEVER DO A **DAY'S WORK** IF THEY CAN HELP IT... ...THEY DON'T KNOW THE MEANING OF THE WORD '**FLAP**'... NO BRAINS, JUST **MASSIVE WINGSPANS**... DON'T GET ME WRONG —I'M NOT ALBATROSSIST, IT'S A **CULTURAL THING**...

OOH **LOOK!** IT'S THE FAMOUS **SOAPBOX!!**

— ©Steve Bell 1997 —

BOING

GOOD MORNING LUTON!

THIS IS REDDITCH!

LET'S KILL HIM!!

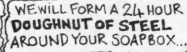

140

142

144

147

WHAT ARE YOU GOING TO **DO** NOW YOU'VE BEEN MADE A **GOVERNMENT MINISTER?**

IT WAS THE **STRIPWOT WON IT**

I SHALL **BEAM**, THEN I SHALL **GLOAT**, THEN IT'S DOWN TO THE SERIOUS BUSINESS OF TACKLING THE **REAL ENEMY!**

WHAT'S THAT? APATHY? SLEAZE? THE FRENCH? GLOBAL INJUSTICE? COMPLACENCY? **WORLD HUNGER?**

NAH — **HARRIET HARMAN!**

I READ HUGO 'GOTCHA' YOUNG

© Steve Bell 1997

STONE ME! IT'S THE **P.L.P.** - LOOK AT THEM ALL!

MOVE 'EM OUT!

ROPE 'EM UP!

9·5·4112·

THERE'S BLEEDIN' **HUNDREDS OF 'EM!**

CRACK

RIDE 'EM IN!

RAWHIDE!

© Steve Bell '97

LURNCH!

STOP THEM **DOGIES!**

LU·U·U·NCH!

LUNCH!

HEY MANDY! THESE HERE WON'T STAND STILL AN' TAKE A WHUPPIN'!

HELL! THEY'RE GITTIN' AWAY!

BUSY MORNING, DARLING DARLING?

YES, DARLING DARLING, I'M ORFF TO THE MINISTRY, THEN LUNCH WITH **TOP CIVIL SERVANTS...**

...FOLLOWED BY DRINKS WITH MY **FRONT BENCH TEAM,** THEN ORFF TO THE HICE, WHERE I'M BEING SWORN IN AS A **PEER OF THE REALM.**

GOSH, DARLING DARLING!!

...IN THAT CASE WHAT ARE YOU **WAITING FOR,** DARLING?

MY **MINISTERIAL ROVER,** OF COURSE. AH! HERE IT IS!

DRING

CIAO, DARLING DARLING!

I HATE **FOOKIN' PENGUINS!**

VITALLY IMPORTANT DOCUMENTS OF STATE

WHERE TO, DUCKFACE? THE MIN. AG. FISH, AND **MAKE IT SNAPPY!!**

IMPORTANT DOCUMENTS OF STATE

SNAPPY? SNAPPY? I'M **NOT A DOG,** Y'KNOW!

YOU'RE NOT? I MEAN, **OF COURSE** YOU'RE NOT...

© Steve Bell '97

I'M IN CHARGE! WHAT I SAY **GOES!!** I'M **NOT** A **FOOKIN' DOG!** NOW, **WHERE TO?**

ER... THE MINISTRY OF AGRICULTURE, AND IF YOU'RE QUICK THERE'S A **BISCUIT** IN IT!

Panel 1: GOOD LORD DARLING! WE'VE BEEN TOGETHER ALL THESE YEARS AND I NEVER REALISED YOU WERE A **TOP FLIGHT BARRISTER!**

WHO'S WHO WEEKLY

WHO'S WHO IN WHO'S WHOLAND

Panel 2: AND I NEVER KNEW YOU HAD IT IN YOU TO BE A **GOVERNMENT MINISTER** AND MEMBER OF THE **HOUSE OF LORDS!**

HAPPY DARLING?

Panel 3: YES DARLING, **VERY** DARLING, BY THE WAY DARLING...

Panel 4: DOES THIS MEAN YOU'RE GOING TO STOP **SHITTING ON THE FURNITURE?**

NO DARLING!

TAXIDERMIST

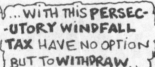

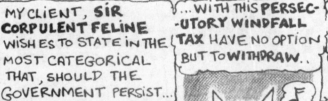

Panel 1: MY CLIENT, **SIR CORPULENT FELINE** WISHES TO STATE IN THE MOST CATEGORICAL THAT, SHOULD THE GOVERNMENT PERSIST...

Panel 2: ...WITH THIS **PERSECUTORY WINDFALL TAX** HAVE NO OPTION BUT TO WITHDRAW...

Panel 3: ...FROM HIS POSITION AS CHIEF ADVISER ON **SOCIAL SECURITY BENEFIT REFORM**...

NO MORE MISTER MICE GUY!

Panel 4: ...FOR **HE CAN DO NO OTHER.**

CAT OF PRINCIPLE

BARP!

I STAND FOR THE RIGHTS OF MICE

Panel 1: AHHH — GORDON COULD I HAVE A **BRIEF WORD?**

Panel 2: WAIT UP, GORDON! I'VE ONLY GOT **SHORT LEGS!**

Panel 3: WHAT'S ALL THIS I HEAR ABOUT YOU REFUSING TO **DRESS UP AS A PENGUIN??**

Panel 1: **MY GOD!** IF I WEAR THIS THERE'LL BE A **RUN ON THE POOND!!**

SEAWEED BROS   SEAWEED BROS

Panel 2: NAH! COBBLERS! IT'S TRADITIONAL! SHOW 'EM YOU'RE MORE THAN JUST A **STUFFED DUMMY!!**

© Steve Bell 1997

Panel 3: ****THE POOND! SHOW 'EM YOU'RE A **STUFFED DUMMY** WITH **BRASS KNOBS ON!**

SUITS YOU, SIR!

I'M NOT SURE — I'LL HAVE TO ASK EDDIE!!

152

BLUBBYBLOBBYBLA BLABBETYBLAIR BLAH BLUB BLEBBABLAY?

BUBLUBLORBLUBBERY BLABLIBABLOBBLUB BLEBBERDEBBABLIBADIB BLOBABLEBLEH?

BLIBBERBLUR BLEBBER !!!

BLAGENG! BLAGENG!

BLAIRYBUBBIES

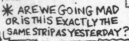
* ARE WE GOING MAD OR IS THIS EXACTLY THE SAME STRIP AS YESTERDAY?

* YOUR SHORT TERM MEMORY HAS BEEN DESTROYED BY TELEVISION + FIZZY DRINKS SO WHAT DO YOU CARE?

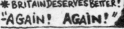
* BRITAIN DESERVES BETTER! "AGAIN! AGAIN!"

I'M A LITTLE TEAPOT, SHORT AND STOUT...

HERE'S MY HUNDLE HERE'S MY SPOUT...

...WHEN IT'S TORY TEATIME, HEAR THE PARTY SHOUT:

"STRING HIM UP AND BURN HIM OUT!!"

16·6·4128

© Steve Bell 1997

MARRY ME AND YOUR LIFE WILL BE ONE LONG PHOTO-OPPORTUNITY!

THAT RHYMES! WILLIAM - YOU'RE SO TALENTED

I'M A BUT OUT OF HELL ♫ WITH LONG TROUSERS AS WELL...

OH WILLIAM - DO YOU KNOW WHAT I LOVE ABOUT YOU MOST?

I KNOW DEAR - IT'S MY KNEES, ISN'T IT?

WOULD YOU MIND GOING DOWN ON ALL FOURS, MISS JENKINS?

SWOON

17·6·4129

DECISIONS, DECISIONS!

SHOULD I STICK WITH MY HARD-LINE SHORTS?

OR SHOULD I PUT ON MY SOFT PROFILE/ONE NATION/ NOTHING RULED IN/NOTHING RULED OUT/NEVER SAY NEVER AT THE END OF THE DAY TROUSERS??

©Steve Bell '97 - 18·6·4130 -

154

155

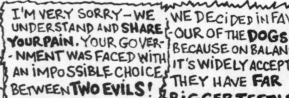

157

WILLIAM
HAGUE
IS
SON OF UNDERPANTS
IN
**NIGHT
OF THE
LONG
TROUSERS**